Sound Matters

Music book

Sound Matters
Music Book   ED 12351
                                        ISBN 0 946535 13 2
Teacher's Manual   ED 12352
(including Pupils' Questions)   ISBN 0 946535 14 0
Music Cassettes   ED 12353MC
Compact Discs   ED 12353CD

Sound Matters

*An anthology of listening material
for GCSE music*

David Bowman
and
Bruce Cole

MUSIC BOOK

ED 12351

SCHOTT
EDUCATIONAL
PUBLICATIONS

Mainz • London • Madrid • New York • Paris • Tokyo • Toronto

Acknowledgements

The publisher wishes to thank the following for their generosity
in allowing the use of their material in this publication:

Anthology No. 2
reprinted by kind permission of Macmillan Publishers Ltd
Anthology No. 3
reprinted by kind permission of the English Folk Dance and Song Society
Anthology Nos. 36 & 45
reproduced by permission of Peters Edition Ltd., London
Anthology No. 38
reprinted by permission of Theodore Presser Co, Pennsylvania
Anthology No. 39
reprinted by permission of Universal Edition (Alfred A. Kalmus Ltd)
Anthology Nos. 40, 42 & 46
reprinted by permission of Boosey and Hawkes Music Publishers Ltd
Anthology No. 41
reprinted by permission of CPP/Belwin Europe
Anthology No. 43
reproduced by permission of Editions A. Leduc, Paris/United Music Publishers Ltd
Anthology No. 44
reprinted by permission of Universal Edition (London) Ltd
Anthology No. 48
reprinted by permission of John Casken
Anthology No. 49
reprinted by permission of Steve Martland
Anthology No. 53
reproduced by permission of EMI Music Publishing Ltd
Anthology No. 53
for Canadian territory reproduced by permission of Warner/Chappell Music Inc.
Anthology No. 53
for USA territory reproduced by permission of The Richmond Organisation
Anthology No. 54
reprinted by permission of European American Music Corporation (Alfred A. Kalmus Ltd)
Anthology No. 55
reproduced by permission of MCA Music Limited
Anthology No. 56
reproduced by permission of Intersong Music Ltd. & International Music Publications
Anthology No. 57 & Nos. 56 & 61
for USA & Canadian territories reproduced by permission of Hal Leonard Publishing Corporation
Anthology No. 58
reproduced by permission of Rak Publishing Ltd. & International Music Publications
Anthology No. 59
reproduced by permission of Skratch Music & International Music Publications
Anthology No. 60
reproduced by permission of New Town Sound Ltd
Anthology No. 61
reproduced by permission of Chappell Music Ltd, and International Music Publications

British Library Cataloguing in Data
Bowman, David
    Sound matters: an anthology of listening material
    for GCSE music.
    1. Music
    I. Title II. Cole, Bruce
    780
    ISBN 0-946535-13-2

ED 12351
© 1989 Schott & Co. Ltd, London

Designed by Geoffrey Wadsley
Music processed on Musicwriter and printed by
Halstan & Co. Ltd, Plantation Road, Amersham, Bucks HP6 6HJ

Foreword

The criteria for Music in the GCSE may seem revolutionary but they are in fact part of a long and gradual transformation of music in schools. Over the last thirty years subtle changes have been taking place. Little by little, we have moved from students learning *about* music to students learning *through* music. Thus, the principal agents of change have been practical and musical. First, the establishment of instrumental teaching schemes that in turn produced school ensembles, and regional and national youth orchestras. Then, in the classroom, the development of techniques to encourage students to compose.

The focal point for all this activity is, of course, *attentive listening*; and it is that which emerges now as the vital linking element in the GCSE's 'Composing-Performing-Listening' ethic. No-one can get very far on a musical instrument without increasing their aural sensitivity; and it is quite literally impossible to compose music without making choices which rest upon aural discrimination and evaluation. Moreover, as students extend their performing and composing skills they become more acutely aware of the significance of musical detail in the interpretative and creative work of others – the kind of detail which can be a source of great delight and a revelation at both the sensual and the structure level; the inspiration and the mechanism of control.

For 'controlling the medium' is what it's all about, and developing the ability to observe closely what others have done in this context is a major part of perfecting one's own skill. It has often been said that the first piece of advice to give to anyone who wants to be a composer is 'You must listen to a lot of music'; but clearly that applies with equal force to every branch of musical activity. To do it properly – to be able to experience a wide range of music and investigate the variety of style and structure in depth – calls for extensive resources: books, scores and – most importantly – recordings. *Sound Matters* provides exactly that kind of help. It is an authoritative and comprehensive anthology that can be entered and used in many different ways to suit particular requirements of teachers and students in both Primary and Secondary education. I have no doubt that it will be welcomed and well used.

JOHN PAYNTER
Professor of Music
University of York

for our children
Hannah, Jonathan, Katy and Ruth

Contents

To allow for the Pupils' Questions and for teachers who wish to devise their own questions, some of the titles in this publication have been deliberately left incomplete. The full title information and attributes can be found in the contents list of the Teacher's Manual and the Music Recordings inlay card.

Music of the Viennese Classical Composers

Music in the Romantic Period

Music in the Twentieth Century

Jazz and Pop

*Anthology numbers marked with an asterisk have no printed score (see Preface).

World Music

Anthology Nos. 50-61 and 69-71: original transcriptions by Bruce Cole.

Preface

Sound Matters is an anthology of printed and recorded music which, together with the Teacher's Manual, provides comprehensive resource materials for the Listening component of GCSE syllabuses in music. Although this is the primary purpose, *Sound Matters* can be used very effectively in the other two interdependent components of GCSE music, Composing and Performing. The analytical commentaries in the Teacher's Manual go far beyond what is required for Listening, so that they can be used to demonstrate various compositional techniques which pupils could adopt in their own course work. Although there are no references to Performing in the commentaries, it is clear that, with the recordings, the commentaries can throw light upon problems of interpretation and thus help pupils to approach their own performing with more understanding. In this connection, the section on popular music contains unique resources. Sheet music editions of pop music are notoriously inadequate, but in this Anthology special transcriptions have been made from the recordings. These sources will not only allow for more detailed listening but will also provide models for composition.

Those who teach music at Advanced Level will be aware of the way in which the resources of *Sound Matters* can be used in preparation for Part II of the Inter-board Test of Aural Perception. For example, Nos. 16a and 16b of the Anthology together form a ready-made 'Comparison', a skeleton score could easily be constructed from any of the items on the lines of those provided in the Classical section of the Pupils' Questions and, perhaps most obviously, the comprehensive commentaries provide what are, in effect, mark schemes for stylistic analysis.

Sound Matters covers all periods and all of the most important styles from 1550 to the present day. The collection begins with simple folk songs, moves chronologically from Palestrina through to a recent BBC TV project, and retraces the twentieth century through Jazz and Pop and ends with ten extracts representing major non-western musical tradition. Although this order could be followed in a listening course, the Anthology has been designed to be flexible enough to meet the needs of teachers who prefer different approaches. For example, the Introduction to the Teacher's Manual

suggests a scheme which moves from the particular to the general, from simple rudiments to broad stylistic generalizations: a complete course with detailed references to the music and commentaries is set out for this. Yet another approach might be to work from the known, be it steel drums or Beethoven, and then move away gradually into the unknown. In this case teachers will find the comprehensive index, which covers the requirements for all GCSE syllabuses, an invaluable tool. The scores in the Music Book have been especially edited so as to avoid needless problems for GCSE students, but great care has been taken to ensure that they accurately reflect not only the composers' intentions but also the performances on the recordings.

Transcriptions have not been provided for some electronic and world music examples (Anthology Nos. 47, 62–68 and the tape part of No. 49), since, for the purposes of this publication, the result might be unrepresentative, misleading and unnecessarily complex. With the exception of some copyright works, non-Italian musical terms and instrument names have been given in English.

In addition to the commentaries, glossary and index the Teacher's Manual includes a separate book of specimen questions on one or two aspects of each piece. These are of two types: a) questions to be answered without the printed music and b) more detailed questions, to be answered with the printed music. The level of difficulty of these questions is determined by the inherent difficulty of the music itself. Teachers may make copies of these questions to distribute to their pupils for use in class or for homework. No attempt has been made to cover all aspects of each piece, and experienced teachers may well choose to disregard some of the questions and replace them with others that they have composed themselves.

It cannot be too strongly stressed that *Sound Matters* is not a course for GCSE music. It is a comprehensive collection of resource materials from which teachers can devise their own courses suited to the needs of particular pupils. It leaves absolute freedom to decide which pieces will be taught, the order in which they will be taught and how they will be taught.

1. Quittez, pasteurs

Old French carol

Quit - tez, pas - teurs, Vos bre - bis, vos hou - let - tes, Vo - tre ha - meau, Et le soin du trou - peau; Chan - gez vos pleurs En u - ne joie par - fai - te; Al - lez tous a - do - rer Un Dieu, un Dieu, un Dieu qui vient vous con - so - ler.

2. Pierlala

18th century Dutch song

Komt hier al' bij, aan - hoort dees Klucht: Het is van Pier - la - la, Een drol - lig vent - jen vol ge - nucht, De vreugd van zijn pa - pa. Wat in zijn le - ven is ges - chied, Dat zult gij hoo - ren in dit lied: 'tIs al van Pier - la - la, sa! sa! 'tIs al van Pier - la - la.

Van Duyse 'Het oude Nederlandsche Lied', The Hague, 1900, No. 322, quoted in Grove 5th edition, volume 3, page 321, article by August Corbet.
Reproduced by permission of The Macmillan Press Ltd.

3. One night as I lay on my bed

Old Dorsetshire folk song

One night as I lay on my bed, I dreamed a - bout a pret - ty maid. I was so dis - tressed I could take no rest; Love did tor - ment me so. So a - way to my true love I did go.

4. Duck Dance

American Muskogean Indian

Bass

Wee ya hay ya wee hee ya hay ya wee hee ya wa hay ya,

Wee hee ya hay ya, Wee ya hay ya wee hee ya hay ya

wee hee ya wa hay ya, Wee hee ya hay ya

wee hee ya wa hay ya, Wee hee ya hay ya. Ho - ke - lay Hoh!

Music in the Late Renaissance

5. La Mourisque

Tielman Susato

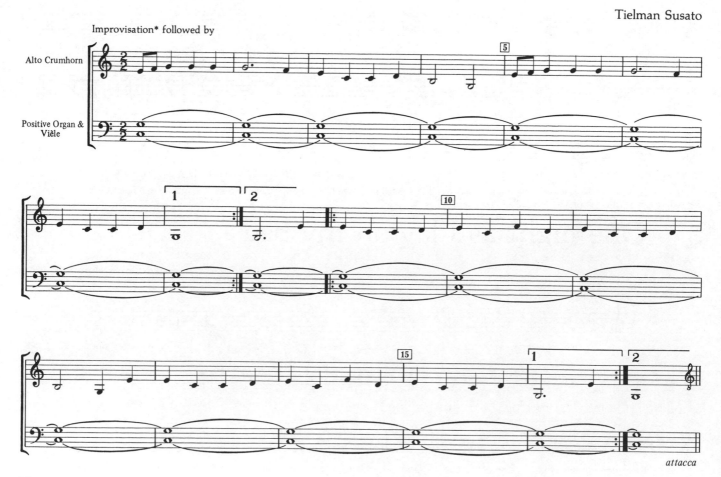

Improvisation* followed by

Alto Crumhorn

Positive Organ & Vièle

attacca

*The opening improvisation, the percussion parts and the ornamentation in the repeats are omitted from this score.

6. Benedictus

Giovanni Pierluigi da Palestrina

NB This movement is performed at a lower pitch than that given in this score.

7. O quam gloriosum est regnum

Tomás Luis da Victoria

8. You that wont, to my pipe's sound

Thomas Morley

NB   The lute part is not notated in this score.

9. Deus in adjutorium

Claudio Monteverdi

* $\mathbf{d} = \mathbf{d}\cdot$ means that the minim beat in $\mathbf{\frac{2}{2}}$ is at the same speed as the dotted minim in $\mathbf{\frac{6}{4}}$, and vice versa at bar 11.

10. Sarabande *from Op. 2 No. 10*

Arcangelo Corelli

11. Hark, each tree *from Ode for St Cecilia's Day*

Henry Purcell

[13]

Hark,   hark each   tree   its

Hark,   hark each   tree   its

si   -   -   -   lence__ breaks

[14]

[15]

12. Second Allegro *from Op. 3 No. 11*

[16]

[18]

[19]

NB   On the accompanying cassette this movement is performed at a lower pitch than that given in this score.

[24]

13. Lascia ch'io pianga *from Rinaldo*

George Frideric Handel

14. Meine Tage in den Leiden *from BWV 150*

Johann Sebastian Bach

NB   On the accompanying cassette this movement is performed at a lower pitch than that given in this score.

15. Seufzer, Tränen, Kummer, Not *from BWV 21*

Johann Sebastian Bach

Seuf - zer, Trä - nen, Kum - mer, Not, ___ Seuf - zer,

Trä - nen, ängst - lich's Seh - nen, Furcht und Tod ___ na - gen mein ___ be - klemm - tes

* ⌢ 2nd time only

[28]

16a. Erschienen ist der herrliche Tag *from BWV 145*

Johann Sebastian Bach

Er - schie - nen ist der herr - lich' Tag, d'ran sich Nie - mand g'nug

freu - en mag: Christ, un - ser Herr,___ heut tri - um - phirt, all' sein' Feind'

er ge - fang - en führt. Hal - le - lu - jah.

16b. Erschienen ist der herrliche Tag, *BWV 629*

Johann Sebastian Bach

NB   The pause marks in both 16a and 16b indicate ends of phrases rather than a significant lengthening of the note values.

17.   Le Petit-Rien

François Couperin

Clavecin

*lightly

[31]

1er COUPLET

RONDEAU

2eme COUPLET

RONDEAU

18. Polonaise *from BWV 1067*

Johann Sebastian Bach

19. Recitatives and Chorus *from Part 1 of Messiah*

George Frideric Handel

RECITATIVE
Secco

Soprano

And the an - gel said un -to them: Fear not;   for be - hold,   I bring   you good

Basso continuo

S.

tid - ings   of great joy,   which shall be   to   all   peo - ple.   For un - to you   is born this

B.c.

day   in the ci - ty of   Da - vid,   a   sa - viour,   which is Christ   the   Lord.

ACCOMPAGNATO

Allegro

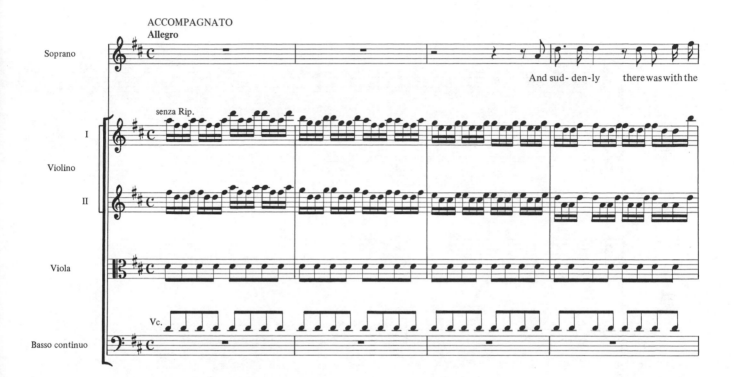

And sud - den - ly   there was with the

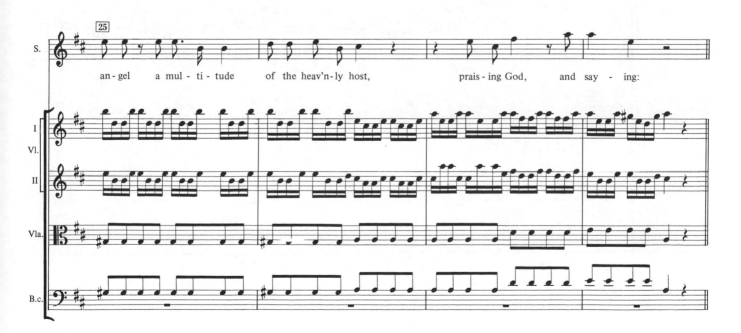

an - gel a mul - ti - tude of the heav'n - ly host,   prais - ing God,   and say - ing:

[35]

CHORUS

[37]

[40]

good - will _____ to - wards men, to - wards men, good - will _____

men, to - wards men, good - will _____ to - wards men, to - wards

to - wards men, good - will _____ to - wards

good - will _____ to - wards men,

7   3   4   6   7   6
          2

[41]

NB   The performance on the accompanying cassette is at a lower pitch than that printed here.

20. Minuet and Trio *from "La Passione"*

Joseph Haydn

Menuet da Capo

21. Poco Adagio *from Op. 9 No. 5*

Joseph Haydn

VARIATION 2

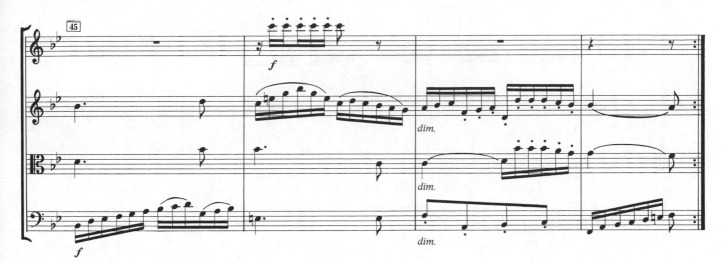

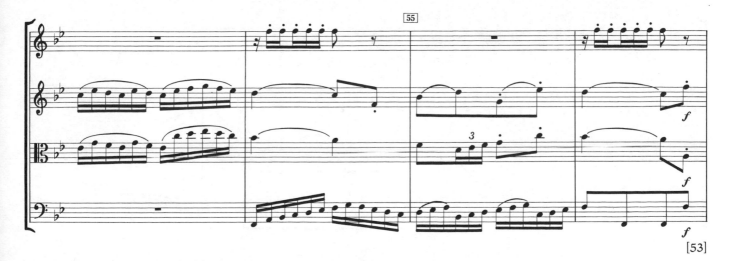

[53]

VARIATION 3

VARIATION 4

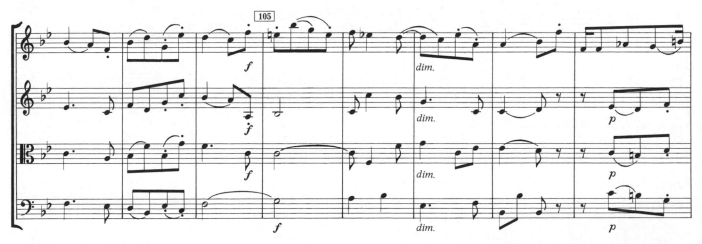

22. Coda *from Larghetto of K.491*

Wolfgang Amadeus Mozart

[59]

[60]

23. Der Vogelfänger *from Die Zauberflöte*

Wolfgang Amadeus Mozart

During the orchestral prelude to this song Papageno comes down a footpath with a huge birdcage on his back. He is covered with feathers and plays on Panpipes as he enters.

1., 2. Der__ Vo - gel - fän - ger__ bin ich ja, stets__ lus - tig hei - sa hop - sa - sa! Ich
3. Wenn al - le Mäd - chen__ wä - ren mein, so__ tausch - te ich brav Zuk - ker ein: die,

(on stage)

Vo - gel - fän - ger_ bin be - kannt bei Alt und Jung im gan - zen Land.
wel - che_ mir am_ lieb - sten wär', der gäb' ich gleich den Zuk - ker her.

(1.) Weiss_ mit dem Lok - ken_ um - zu - gehn und mich auf's Pfei - fen_
(2.) Ein_ Netz für Mäd - chen_ möch - te ich, ich fing' sie dut - zend -
(3.) Und_ küss - te sie_ mich_ zärt - lich dann, wär' sie mein Weib_ und_

[66]

zu ver - stehn.
- weis' für mich!
ich ihr Mann.

D'rum_ kann ich froh und_ lus - tig sein, denn_
Dann_ sperr - te ich_ sie_ bei mir ein, und_
Sie_ schlief' an mei - ner_ Sei - te ein, ich_

al - le Vö - gel_ sind ja_ mein.
al - le Mäd - chen_ wä - ren_ mein.
wieg - te wie_ ein_ Kind sie_ ein.

[67]

24. Andante *from Sonata Op. 49 No. 1*

Ludwig van Beethoven

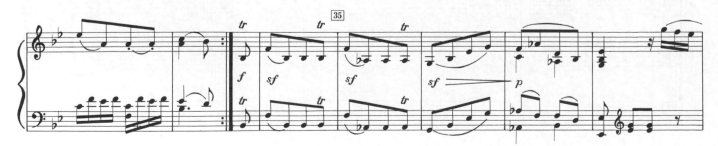

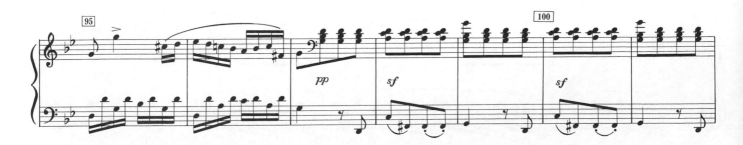

25. Overture *from Der Freischütz*

Carl Maria von Weber

26. Am Meer *from Schwanengesang*

Franz Schubert

Das Meer er-glänz-te weit hin-aus im letz-ten A - bend-

-schei - ne. Wir sas - sen am ein - sa - men Fi - scher - haus, wir sas - sen stumm und al -

- lei - ne. Der Ne - bel stieg,

das Was - ser schwoll, die Mö - we flog hin und wie - der.

Aus dei - nen Au - gen lie - be - voll fie - len die Trä - nen

nie - der. Ich sah sie fal - len auf dei - ne Hand und

bin aufs Knie ge - sun - ken. Ich hab von dei - ner___ weis - sen Hand die

Trä - nen fort - ge - trun - ken. Seit je - ner Stun - de

ver - zehrt sich mein Leib, die See - le stirbt vor Seh - nen.

Mich hat das un - glück - sel - ge Weib___ ver -

- gif - tet mit ih - ren___ Trä - nen.

NB   Originally written in C. The performance on the accompanying cassette is in B flat.

[75]

27. Un Bal *from Symphonie fantastique*

Hector Berlioz

*The sign ⌣ indicates that the sound must glide from note to note (Berlioz), i.e. *portamento*.

[78]

28. Mazurka *Op. 7 No. 5*

Frédéric Chopin

29. Fantasiestuck *Op. 73 No. 1*

Robert Schumann

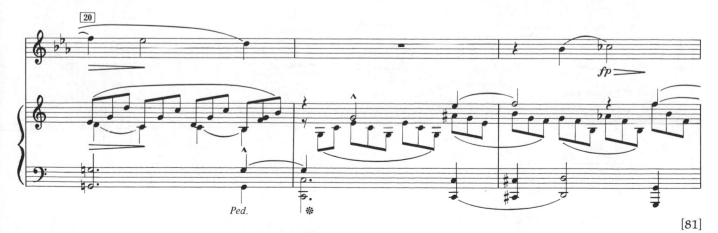

[81]

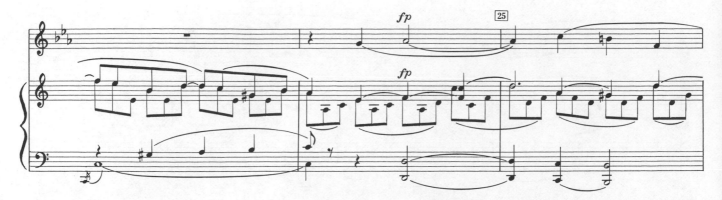

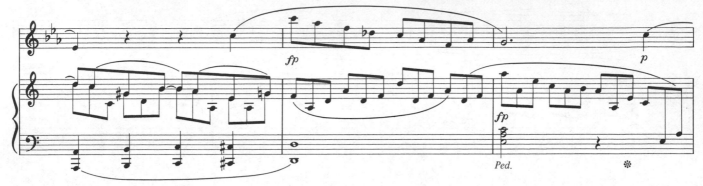

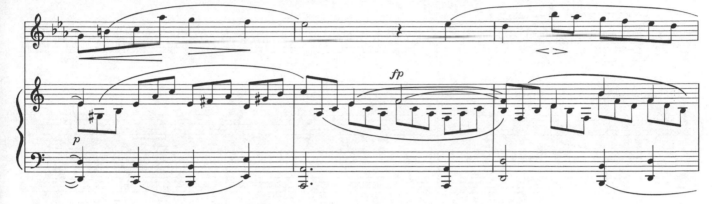

30. Preludio *from Études d'exécution transcendante*

Franz Liszt

Pianoforte

31. Miserere *from Il Trovatore*

Giuseppe Verdi

[87]

[88]

[89]

32. Prelude *to Tristan and Isolde*

Richard Wagner

33. Variations 13-16 *from the Finale of Symphony No. 4*

Johannes Brahms

(VARIATION 14)

(VARIATION 15)

[95]

(VARIATION 16) 130

*Fast, powerful and ardent.

[96]

34. Dumka *from Piano Quintet in A, Op. 81*

Antonin Dvořák

35. Slow movement *from Symphony No. 5*

Peter Ilyich Tchaikovsky

*At a moderate speed, in a singing style and with much freedom.

36. Epilog *from Till Eulenspiegel*

Richard Strauss

[103]

37. Voiles *from Préludes, Book I*

Claude Debussy

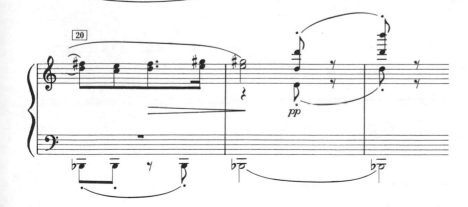

38. The Anti-Abolitionist Riots in the 1830's and 1840's

Charles E. Ives
Edited by Henry Cowell

39. Third movement *from Variations for Piano Op. 27*

Anton Webern

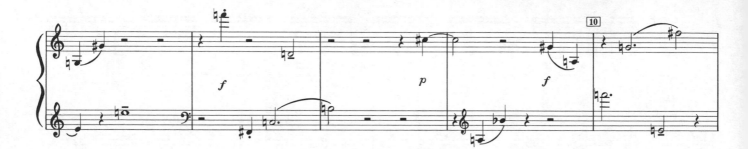

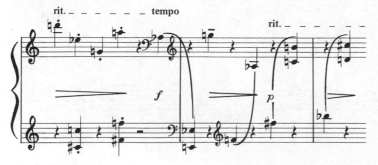

*gently flowing

40. Third movement *from Sonata for two pianos and percussion*

Béla Bartók

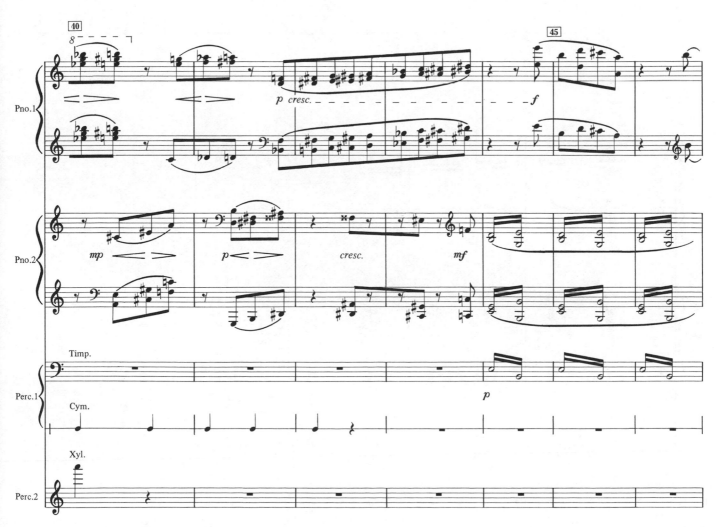

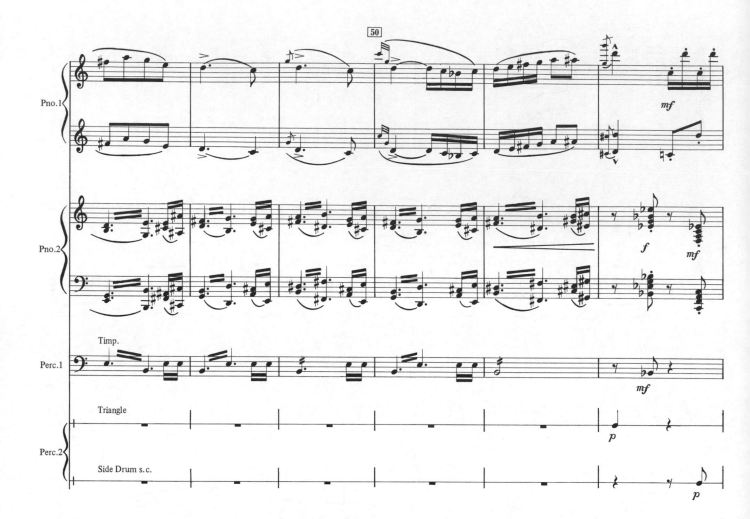

41. Secondo *from String Quartet No. 6*

Elisabeth Lutyens

[115]

42. Bransle Simple *from Agon*

Igor Stravinsky

[116]

[120]

43. Le Traquet Stapazin *from Catalogue d'oiseaux*

Olivier Messiaen

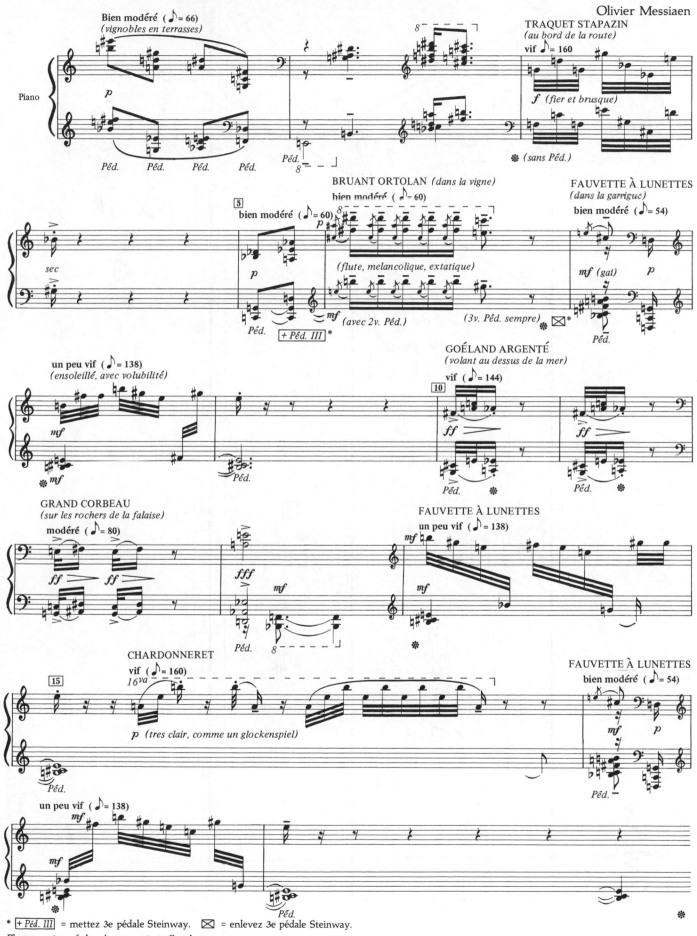

44. Zyklus

Karlheinz Stockhausen

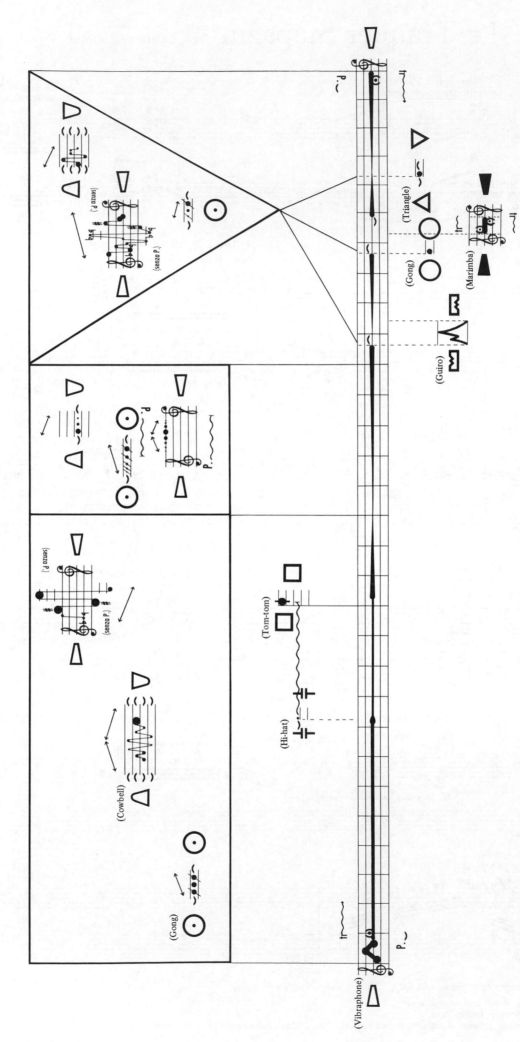

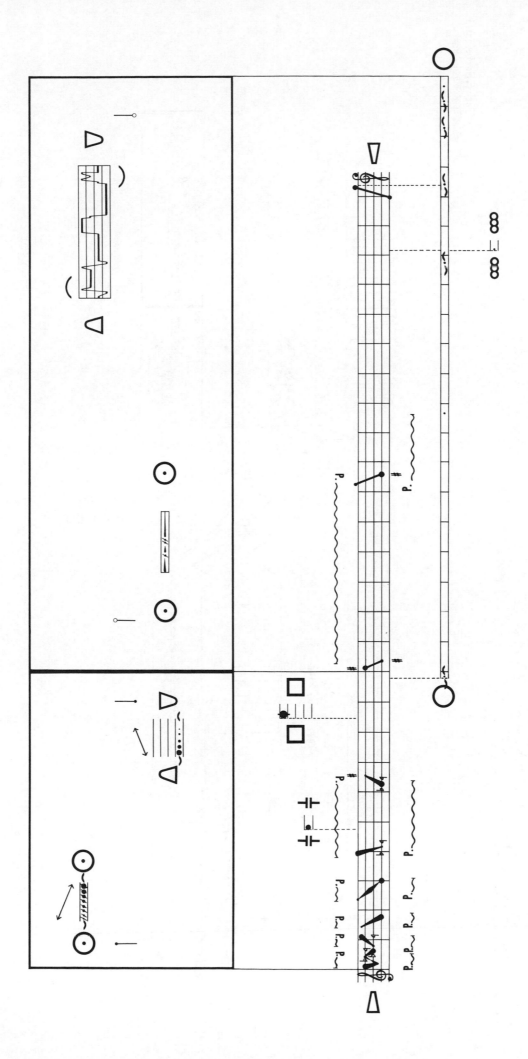

45. Stripsody

Cathy Berberian
Graphics by Roberto Zamarin

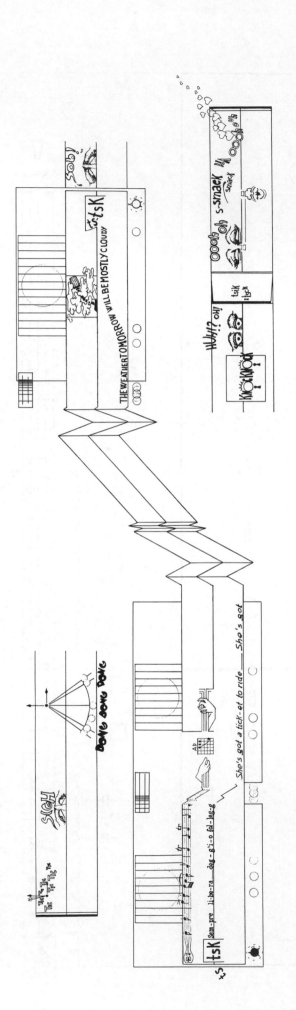

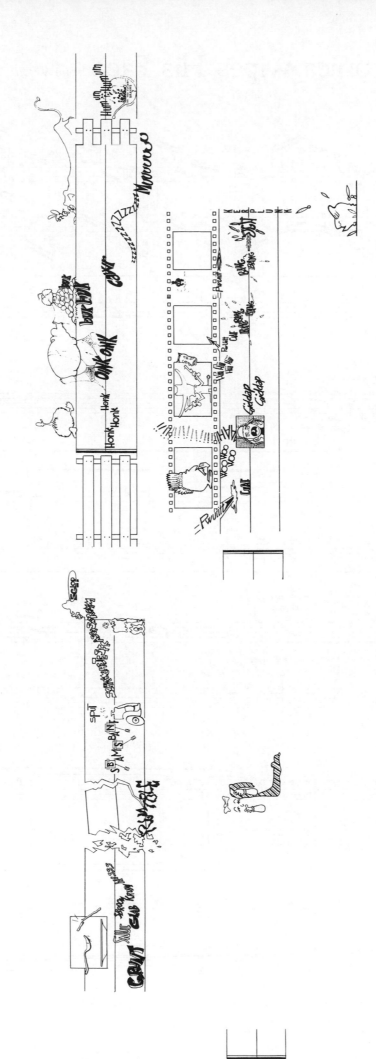

46. St Veronica wipes His Face *from Vesalii Icones*

Peter Maxwell Davies

*The pianist records bars 259–262 (as far as the downbeat) on a cheap commercial tape recorder, (during performance with cellist).

© Copyright 1978 Boosey & Hawkes Music Publishers Ltd.
Reproduced by permission of Boosey & Hawkes Music Publishers Ltd.

The pianist starts music-box at 3rd measure of tape-recording and fades tape at Conductor's direction.

Musicians imitate quietly motifs of music-box, Vla. and Vc. pizz. Percussion has Glockenspiel.

Pianist stops music-box at Conductor's direction: Fade out: pause.

48. Piper's Linn *for Northumbrian Small Pipes and pre-recorded tape*

John Casken

The number of repeats for each bar is approximate and will vary according to performance.

repeat to 10'06" and stop
at beginning of new section

(repeat *presto*, until climax begins
to recede at *c.* 12'40'')

*Retain essential rhythm, but insert longer commas (,) between repeats.

[131]

49. The World is in Heaven *from Glad Day*

Music by Steve Martland
Words by Stevan Keane

VERSE 1º

Hi-hat

Dr. Mach.

V.

1. When ev' - ry mo - ment is sto - len, These days have no life of their

B.Gt.

30

Dr. Mach.

Hand-clap

V.

own; There is no time— like the pre - sent, The

B.Gt.

VERSE 2º

Dr. Mach.

V.

lights are on but no - one's home; 2. This is no sea - son for

B.Gt.

These are the days Mam-mon an - ti - ci - pat - ed, These are the days when the gaunt - let is run, but the

sing - ing will ne - ver be done, for as ev - er

[136]

50. Peace in the Valley

Flora Molton
traditional

Voice

Guitar

freely

Tambourine

5 ♩ = *c.* **80** *Spoken:*

This is a song, very sad song. Peace in the Valley. It's sad to make about the time I lost my father. My sister-in-law, she passed late about a few days ago. But anyhow, she went on train with the body, and my brother and I drove through the mountains and (there we are) driving along we heard this song on the radio.

repeat freely through introduction

repeat freely through introduction

14 Come and sing it. I am tired I am

15 wor-ried but I must go on. Tell the Lord __ He shall call __ me a-

20 - way { I tell my brother. He screamed and he woke me up. I was right. } But the morn-ing is so bright, __ and the land is a-

25 - live, __ and the sky __ is as clear __ as __ the day, oh __ there'll be peace. __

[137]

51. Fidgety Feet

Original Dixieland Jazz Band
(La Rocca/Edwards/Shields/Ragas/Sbarbaro)

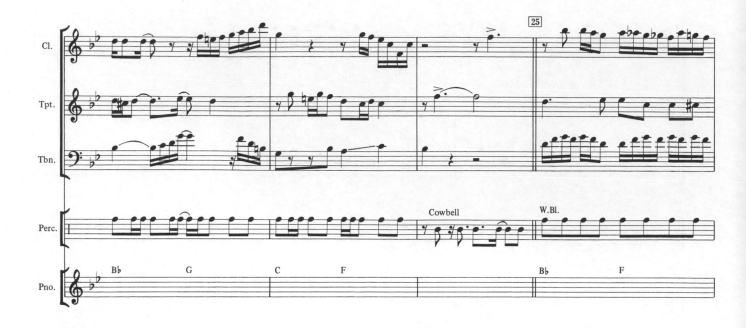

[140]

52. Jazz Me Blues

Bix Beiderbecke and his Gang
Composed by Delaney

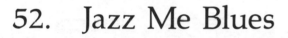

[144]

[145]

53. Only You

The Platters
Words and Music by Ande Rand and Buck Ram

54. Mack the Knife

Ella Fitzgerald
Music by Kurt Weill
Words by Marc Blitzstein
(Original words by Bertolt Brecht)

Sun-day morn - ing ___ lies a bo - dy ooz - - - ing ___ life

___ some-one ___ sneak - ing 'round ___ that cor - ner ___ tell me could it

be could it be could it be____ Mack____ the____ knife? On____ a____

____ tug boat down by____ the ri-ver don't you know____ a ce - ment bag's

55. The Girl from Ipanema

(Garota De Ipanema)
Stan Getz and Astrud Gilberto
Music by Antonio Carlos Jobin
English words by Norman Gimbel
Original words by Vinicius de Moraes

when she pass - es he smiles___ but she does - n't see___

56. Papa's Got a Brand New Bag

James Brown and the Famous Flames
Words and Music by James Brown

Well come here___ an' dig this cra - zy scene___

It's not too bad___ there but it's fine as it can be,___

[160]

shy___ You do the mon-key mashed po - ta - to, jump back Jack___ see you la - ter al - li - ga-

- tor, Come down sis - ter___ Pa-pa's in the swing___

If you're hip now,_____ well I can dig the new breed__ sing,__

Ain't no drag _____ he's got a brand new bag.__

57. Purple Haze

The Jimi Hendrix Experience
Words and Music by Jimi Hendrix

58. Music

John Miles
Words and Music by John Miles
Orchestration by Andrew Powell

[167]

[170]

'Cause in this world of trou - bles   my mu - sic pulls me

59. Easier Said than Done

Shakatak
Words and Music by William Sharpe
and Roger Odell

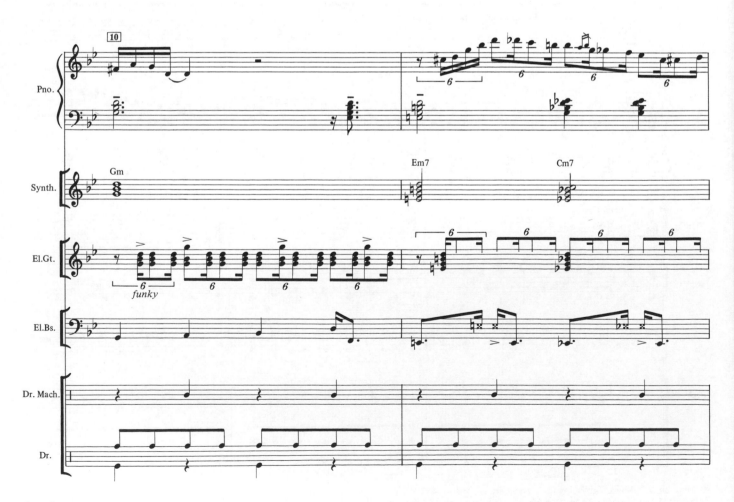

60.   I and I are the Chosen One

Prince Far I
Words and Music by Michael Williams

Spoken: Goliath has slain one thousand, David has slain ten thousand, 'cos I and I Are the Chosen One from Africa. I depend on Jah only, my Salvation come from him. He is the only One, I protector,

I Saviour, I Defender, I shall never be defeated.

How much longer will all of you like a falling wall,
talk among defeated.

like a broken-down fence, You only want to bring him down from his place of honour. You did plagiaring lies. You speak words

echo

61. The Sun Goes Down

Level 42
Words and Music by Mark King, Philip Gould,
Wally Baderou and Michael Lindup

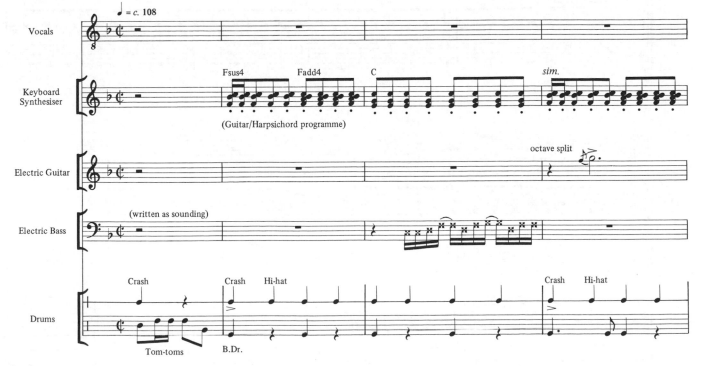

[182]

World Music

69. Jelea Din Bosanci

The Paul Stinga Orchestra
Romania

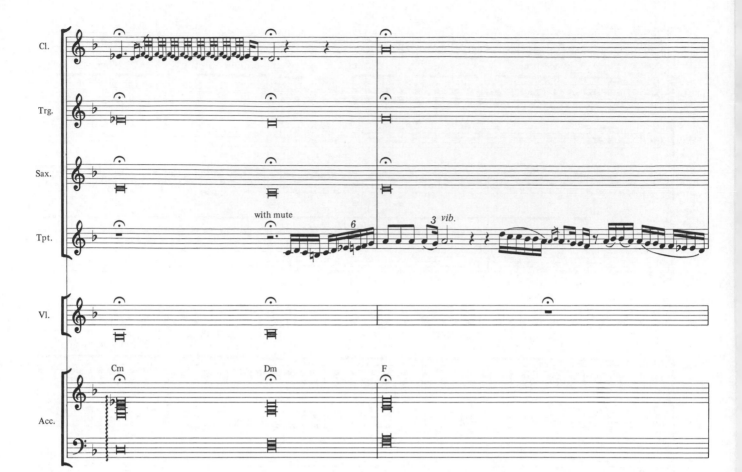

70. Mi Raza

Los Yuras
Bolivia

*These are played as uneven quavers throughout.

71. National

Steel Band
Trinidad

[190]